JUDY SCHA

I Am
Skippyjon
Jones

SCHOLASTIC INC.
New York Toronto London Auckland Sydney
Mexico City New Delhi Hong Kong Buenos Aires

I am **Skippyjon Jones**,
a Chihuahua to my bones.
I can be anything!

I am a great sword fighter.

I am a deep-sea diver.

I am a dinosaur tamer with a loud bark-ito.

I am a fancy dancer!

I am a great artist.

And I can sing, with the music turned up loud.

I am a brave explorer. I can see far and wide.

And I go to the ends of the Earth.

I am a friend to all, large and small.

I am Skippyjon Jones,
a reader to my bones.

**Who will I be next?
I will open this book-ito
and see!**